ROSINSKI–VAN HAMME

THORGAL
The Archers

Translation by Chris Tanz and Jean-Paul Bierny • Edited by Kay Reynolds

ink
PUBLISHING
15 EAST CALLE CONQUISTA
TUCSON ARIZONA 85716

Distributed by The Donning Company / Publishers

Published by Ink Publishing
Distributed by The Donning Company/Publishers

Copyright © 1985 Lombard/Rosinski/Van Hamme
Translation © 1987 by Chris Tanz and Jean-Paul Bierny

For information, write:
  The Donning Company/Publishers
  5659 Virginia Beach Boulevard
  Norfolk, Virginia 23502

Library of Congress Cataloging-in-Publication Data
Van Hamme, Jean, 1939-
   Thorgal, the archers.
   Translation of: Thorgal, les archers.
   Summary: The shipwrecked adventurer Thorgal hopes
to get home with prize money from an archery
competition, but the tournament promises to be both
unchivalrous and dangerous.
   [1. Archery—Fiction. 2. Adventure and adventurers—
Fiction. 3. Cartoons and comics] I. Rosinski, Grzegorz, ill.
II. Title.
PN6790.B43H3713   1987   741.5'9493   [Fic]   87-2645
ISBN 0-9617885-0-X

PSSST...

HERE -- CATCH!

WELCOME ABOARD, FRIEND! LUCKY I WAS HERE, HUNH?

THEY CALL ME TJALL THE RECKLESS, AND YOU?

??

THORGAL AEGIRSSON. DELIGHTED.

6

TWO BOATS SUNK? MY COMPLIMENTS TJALL. YOU'VE OUTDONE YOURSELF.

I'LL NEVER UNDERSTAND HOW YOUR HEAD WORKS. WHAT WERE YOU DOING OUT AT SEA IN WEATHER LIKE THAT?

JUST FELT LIKE SEEING YOU. THAT'S ALL, DEAR UNCLE.

FORGIVE HIM THORGAL. HE MEANS WELL-- BUT HE'S GOT NO MORE SENSE THAN A CLAM. THERE-- THIS SHOULD MAKE IT HEAL FASTER.

IT FEELS BETTER. THANK YOU, ARGHUN.

CALL ME PEG LEG. EVERYONE DOES. YOU'RE NOT FROM AROUND HERE. HAVE YOU TRAVELED FAR?

YES-- AND NO.

I LIVE ON AN ISLAND. I WAS HEADED HOME WHEN THE STORM CAME UP. I DRIFTED ALL DAY AND NIGHT.

WELL, THERE'S A FISHING VILLAGE NEARBY. YOU CAN PROBABLY BUY A NEW BOAT THERE.

IF ONLY I COULD. THE TROUBLE IS MY BOAT SANK WITH EVERYTHING IN IT-- INCLUDING MY WEAPONS AND WHAT LITTLE GOLD I HAD...

11

YOU MAKE
WEAPONS?

YES.
I SPECIALIZE IN
BOWS AND ARROWS--
SOMETHING FOR
EVERY TASTE AND
EVERY
PURPOSE.

THIS IS THE
CLASSIC STYLE
FOR HUNTING. HERE,
A SIMPLE POINT FOR
TARGET PRACTICE...
LAUREL LEAF TO
PIERCE ARMOR...
BALL-HEAD TO STUN.
A WHISTLING HEAD
TO TERRIFY
THE ENEMY.

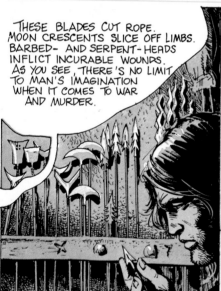

THESE BLADES CUT ROPE.
MOON CRESCENTS SLICE OFF LIMBS.
BARBED- AND SERPENT-HEADS
INFLICT INCURABLE WOUNDS.
AS YOU SEE, THERE'S NO LIMIT
TO MAN'S IMAGINATION
WHEN IT COMES TO WAR
AND MURDER.

WHAT'S
THIS?

AN EXPERIMENT. A BOW
WITH A DOUBLE CURVE
LIKE THEY USE IN THE
ORIENT. IT'S SMALLER
THAN A CLASSIC
BOW BUT TAKES
GREAT STRENGTH
TO DRAW.

CAN YOU USE
A BOW?

A LITTLE...
I'D LIKE TO
TRY THIS WHEN
MY HAND IS
HEALED.

WHY DON'T YOU
COME WITH US TO
UMBRIA?
THE TOURNAMENT WILL
BRING PLENTY OF
CUSTOMERS. I CAN USE
ALL THE HELP I CAN
GET.

I WAS ABOUT
TO SUGGEST IT
MYSELF, PEG
LEG.

...BUT SPEAKING
OF CUSTOMERS, IT
LOOKS LIKE WE'VE
GOT A COUPLE NOW.
AND THEY DON'T
LOOK LIKE RABBIT
HUNTERS!

HMM... I KNOW THOSE TWO...

KRISS OF VALNOR AND SIGWALD-THE-BURNED -- WHAT A PAIR OF GODLESS MERCENARIES.

THEY'D HIRE OUT TO THE REAPER HIMSELF FOR A PRICE.

BUT THAT ONE'S ONLY A YOUNG GIRL!

A DANGEROUS YOUNG GIRL. UNAFRAID OF MAN OR BEAST. THEY SAY THAT WITH HER BOW SHE CAN SLICE THE BEAK OFF A FLYING SPARROW AT FIFTY PACES.

PEG LEG, YOU WORK UP HERE ALONE. DON'T YOU HAVE TROUBLE WITH THIS KIND OF... CUSTOMER?

BANDITS NEED WEAPONS AS MUCH AS SOLDIERS DO. THEIR COIN IS AS GOOD.

AND I TAKE SOME PRECAUTIONS.

SCHLANGGG

WELCOME FRIENDS! DISMOUNT AND THROW YOUR WEAPONS TO THE OTHER SIDE OF THE GRILL! YOU'LL GET THEM BACK ON YOUR WAY OUT.

CAUTIOUS AS ALWAYS, EH, PEG LEG?

LOSING **ONE** LEG WAS ENOUGH, SIGWALD! I THINK I'LL KEEP THE OTHER!

I SUPPOSE YOU'RE COMING TO TAKE PART IN THE TOURNAMENT?

WE'RE COMING TO **WIN** IT, KID.

LET'S NOT WASTE TIME. WHERE CAN WE TEST THESE ARROWS?

HERE YOU'LL BE OUT OF THE WIND. THE DISTANCE IS FORTY PACES.

WHAT A GORGEOUS GIRL!

SHE'S A WILDCAT, TJALL. WATCH OUT FOR HER CLAWS.

PERFECT
BALANCE,
PEG LEG --
AS
USUAL!

YOU --
WITH THE
CRIPPLED
HAND! SPIN THE
WHEEL!

WELL,
WHAT ARE YOU
WAITING
FOR!?

AT YOUR
COMMAND,
PRINCESS.

GOOD,
KRISS!

VERY
GOOD! AND
YOUR
SPEED --

WELL ...
IT WASN'T
BAD.

BUT ONE
ARROW ISN'T
CENTERED.

YOU CAN DO
BETTER,
I SUPPOSE?

WOULD YOU
SPIN
THE WHEEL
AGAIN,
THORGAL?

15

THERE!

PAY FOR THE ARROWS AND LET'S GET OUT OF HERE, SIGWALD!

YOU DID **NOT** WIN YOURSELF A FRIEND, TJALL THE RECKLESS.

YOU'RE A FINE MARKSMAN... BUT IT'S NOT SMART TO SHOW YOUR STRENGTH BEFORE THE BATTLE. ESPECIALLY TO SOMEONE LIKE HER.

I'M NOT WORRIED...

NOW I'VE GOT **TWO** GOOD REASONS TO GO TO UMBRIA!

"WE'VE GOT COMPANY..."

"BANDITS BY THE LOOK OF THEM. JUST HOLD YOUR GROUND."

DID YOU SEE THAT? KRISS' JEWEL!

STOP! YES, I SAW!

LISTEN, TJALL. THOSE MEN WOULD HAVE TO BE PART OF A MUCH LARGER GROUP TO TAKE KRISS AND SIGWALD. YOU KNOW THE KIND OF PEOPLE THEY ARE. WOLVES DEVOUR EACH OTHER.

I WON'T LEAVE HER!

GO ON WITHOUT ME! I'M GOING TO SAVE KRISS IF SHE'S STILL ALIVE. IF NOT, THEN-- THEN I'LL SEE!

I DON'T BELIEVE WE'RE DOING THIS... THERE'S THE CAMP-- AND THE BANDITS!

I DIDN'T SEE HER ANYWHERE...

BUT WE SAW PLENTY OF ROGUES! KRISS AND SIGWALD ARE PROBABLY **DEAD**! ALL YOUR 'QUEST' IS GOING TO DO IS RUIN MY GOOD LEG!

WE SHOULD WAIT UNTIL DARK AND LOOK CLOSER.

STAY HERE, PEG LEG. WE'RE GOING...

TRY TO KEEP TJALL FROM DOING SOMETHING **STUPID**... IF YOU CAN.

THOSE BANDITS LOOK SO DUMB, I'LL WAGER THEY FORGOT TO POST A LOOK-OUT!

SSHH!

16

TAK

HMPFF...

18

SIGWALD!!

THORGAL!?

YOU ALL RIGHT?

OH YES... WONDERFUL... LIKE A MOUNTAIN FELL ON MY HEAD.

WE HAD SPLIT UP TO GO HUNTING WHEN THEY ATTACKED KRISS. THERE WERE TOO MANY AND I WAS TOO FAR AWAY TO HELP. I'VE BEEN WAITING SINCE YESTERDAY FOR A CHANCE...

SHE NEVER CRIED OUT ONCE -- BUT WHAT THEY DID TO HER...! I COULD TEAR THEM APART WITH MY BARE HANDS!

THERE ARE STILL TOO MANY, SIGWALD. WE MUST WAIT UNTIL THEY'RE ASLEEP, THEN WE'LL SET HER FREE.

19

SO YOU'RE FINISHED -- AND YOU LOOK IT. DON'T KNOW WHY YOU'D WEAR YOURSELVES OUT BURYING THAT SCUM!

STILL, YOU DIDN'T HANDLE YOURSELVES BADLY. SO SIGWALD AND I HAVE DECIDED TO LEAVE YOU HALF OF THESE HORSES. THOSE DOGS WON'T BE NEEDING THEM ANYMORE.

LET'S GO. WE'VE JUST BEEN WASTING OUR TIME.

NO ONE STRIKES KRISS OF VALNOR! I'LL KILL YOU FOR THIS, THORGAL AEGIRSSON!

22

24

PULL!

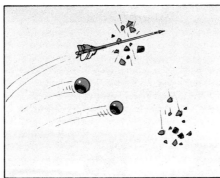

...AND THREE!

GOOD SHOOTING, PEG LEG!

STILL GOT YOUR ARM **AND** YOUR EYE, YOU OLD SOLDIER!

BAH -- IT'S MY **WEAPONS**! THEY DO ALL THE WORK. YOUR TURN, TJALL. DO OUR FAMILY PROUD...

PULL!

25

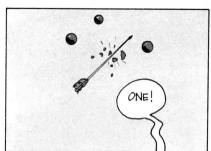

ONE!

...TWO!

GREAT, TJALL!

THANK YOU GENTLE PEOPLE! AND WHEN YOU'RE PLACING YOUR BETS TOMORROW, REMEMBER--

TJALL! WHY DON'T YOU SIGN US UP FOR THE TOURNAMENT INSTEAD OF STRUTTING ABOUT? WE'LL SEE TO THE HORSES AND THE WAGON.

...THREE!

FOUR!

A BRAVE HEART AND A FINE ARCHER... AND THE BRAINS OF A GOOSE! HEH. JUST LIKE ME AT HIS AGE.

NICE SHOOTING, TJALL.

KRISS! DID--DID YOU SEE ME?

MM HMM... I CAN HIT FOUR BALLS TOO. THERE AREN'T MANY--LIKE US-- WHO CAN.

HAVE...HAVE YOU ENTERED YET?

THEY ONLY ACCEPT COMPETITORS IN PAIRS. AND YOU KNOW SIGWALD WAS HURT. TOO BAD...

YOU KNOW, IF WE TEAMED UP, WE COULD BE THE BEST.

PEG LEG IS **OLD**. HE'LL TIRE OUT. IF YOU STICK WITH HIM YOU HAVEN'T GOT A CHANCE.

BUT...BUT, I...

YOU'LL TRY ANYTHING, WON'T YOU?

YOU WANT TO WIN THAT BADLY? FINE. SO DO I.

YOU!?!

YOU WANT TO ENTER THE TOURNAMENT!?

I STILL NEED A BOAT, REMEMBER? BESIDES, MY HAND COULD USE THE EXERCISE.

I SWORE TO **KILL** YOU, **REMEMBER**? I'D RATHER TEAM UP WITH A RAT.

A RAT **WOULD** SUIT YOU BETTER BUT I DON'T THINK YOU CAN AFFORD TO BE CHOOSY. NECESSITY MAKES STRANGE PARTNERS, KRISS.

WHAT MAKES **YOU** THINK **YOU'RE** GOOD ENOUGH TO BE **MY** PARTNER?

WELL... I'VE GOT A **LITTLE** SKILL...

I'LL BELIEVE IT WHEN I SEE IT. IF YOU CAN HIT FOUR BALLS, **I MIGHT** CONSIDER YOU.

GO!... I'M READY FOR A LAUGH...

PULL!

??

!?!

?!...

27

SO -- YOU WIN. BUT DON'T THINK I'LL FORGET HOW YOU HUMILIATED ME. THIS TRUCE LASTS ONLY AS LONG AS THE TOURNAMENT.

YOU KNOW, PEG LEG'S CRAFTSMANSHIP **IS** GOOD!

ALL RIGHT. SEE YOU TOMORROW, **PARTNER.**

FIVE, UNCLE! HE HIT **FIVE** BALLS! I'VE NEVER SEEN **ANYONE** DRAW THAT FAST-- AND WITH A WOUNDED HAND!

KRISS AND THORGAL -- THEY'LL BE HARD TO BEAT ALL RIGHT.

WHERE COULD HE HAVE COME FROM UNCLE? WHAT KIND OF MAN IS HE?

HE'S A MAN, TJALL... JUST A MAN. AND ONE WE SHOULD IMITATE IF WE WANT TO BE IN SHAPE TOMORROW. GOOD NIGHT, MY BOY. SLEEP WELL.

THE EVENTS WILL CONTINUE FOR TWO DAYS IN ORDER OF INCREASING DIFFICULTY. THE LAST TEAM REMAINING IN THE TOURNAMENT WILL BE DECLARED THE WINNERS...

SO-- LET THE CONTEST BEGIN!

GOOD LUCK, THORGAL!

YOU TOO, PEG LEG!

TCHAC TCHAC TCHAC TCHAC TCHAC TCHAC TCHAC

31

TCHAC

TCHAC
TCHAC

DON'T BOTHER -- THEY'RE NOT WORTH IT!

AS FOR THESE **BABES** WHO STROLL OUT OF CAMP UNARMED . . .

WE'RE EVEN NOW, AEGIRSSON! WE'LL SETTLE OTHER ACCOUNTS LATER.

MY THANKS ALL THE SAME.

FOR **WHAT?** YOU'RE MY PARTNER, REMEMBER? I'M JUST PROTECTING MY INTERESTS, THAT'S ALL. AND NOW YOU OUGHT TO TURN IN.

YOU'RE **TOO** KIND -- LOOKING AFTER OUR HEALTH TOO!

YOU WON'T FEEL LIKE LAUGHING TOMORROW -- NOT WHEN **YOU'RE** THE **TARGET.** SKILL ISN'T ENOUGH. YOU'LL NEED **COURAGE** THEN.

17

DID YOU SEE THAT? KRISS' JEWEL!

STOP! YES, I SAW!

LISTEN, TJALL. THOSE MEN WOULD HAVE TO BE PART OF A MUCH LARGER GROUP TO TAKE KRISS AND SIGWALD. YOU KNOW THE KIND OF PEOPLE THEY ARE. WOLVES DEVOUR EACH OTHER.

I WON'T LEAVE HER!

GO ON WITHOUT ME! I'M GOING TO SAVE KRISS IF SHE'S STILL ALIVE. IF NOT, THEN -- THEN I'LL SEE!

I DON'T BELIEVE WE'RE DOING THIS... THERE'S THE CAMP -- AND THE BANDITS!

I DIDN'T SEE HER ANYWHERE...

BUT WE SAW PLENTY OF ROGUES! KRISS AND SIGWALD ARE PROBABLY **DEAD**! ALL YOUR 'QUEST' IS GOING TO DO IS RUIN MY GOOD LEG!

WE SHOULD WAIT UNTIL DARK AND LOOK CLOSER.

STAY HERE, PEG LEG. WE'RE GOING...

TRY TO KEEP TJALL FROM DOING SOMETHING **STUPID**... IF YOU CAN.

THOSE BANDITS LOOK SO DUMB, I'LL WAGER THEY FORGOT TO POST A LOOK-OUT!

SSHH!

16

TAK

HMPFF...

18

SIGWALD!!

THORGAL!?

YOU ALL RIGHT?

OH YES... WONDERFUL... LIKE A MOUNTAIN FELL ON MY HEAD.

WE HAD SPLIT UP TO GO HUNTING WHEN THEY ATTACKED KRISS. THERE WERE TOO MANY AND I WAS TOO FAR AWAY TO HELP. I'VE BEEN WAITING SINCE YESTERDAY FOR A CHANCE...

SHE NEVER CRIED OUT ONCE -- BUT WHAT THEY DID TO HER...! I COULD TEAR THEM APART WITH MY BARE HANDS!

THERE ARE STILL TOO MANY, SIGWALD. WE MUST WAIT UNTIL THEY'RE ASLEEP, THEN WE'LL SET HER FREE.

19

ARE YOU--
I'M FINE! BUT THOSE DOGS WILL PAY! GIVE ME YOUR KNIFE!

HELP! HELP! THEY'RE TAKING ME AWAY!

HA! HA! NOW MY FRIENDS, IF YOU WANT TO LIVE, YOU'LL HAVE TO KILL THEM ALL!

LIKE THIS!

21

SIGWALD, WAIT!

THIS ONE IS MINE! I'VE BEEN WAITING FOR THIS...

...BUT, YOU'RE BLEEDING...

IT'S NOT BAD BUT I WON'T BE ABLE TO USE A BOW FOR A WHILE. UMBRIA'S OVER FOR ME.

THEN HE PAYS FOR THAT, TOO!

THE FIGHT'S OVER, KRISS! STOP! YOU CAN'T GUT A MAN LIKE A --

AAAAAHHHRGGHH

WHAT KIND OF WOMAN IS SHE, SIGWALD? WILD ANIMALS DON'T ACT LIKE THAT.

YOU HAVE NO RIGHT TO JUDGE HER, THORGAL. YOU WEREN'T THEIR PRISONER. LET IT BE.

SO YOU'RE FINISHED -- AND YOU LOOK IT. DON'T KNOW WHY YOU'D WEAR YOURSELVES OUT BURYING THAT SCUM!

STILL, YOU DIDN'T HANDLE YOURSELVES BADLY. SO SIGWALD AND I HAVE DECIDED TO LEAVE YOU HALF OF THESE HORSES. THOSE DOGS WON'T BE NEEDING THEM ANYMORE.

LET'S GO. WE'VE JUST BEEN WASTING OUR TIME.

NO ONE STRIKES KRISS OF VALNOR! I'LL KILL YOU FOR THIS, THORGAL AEGIRSSON!

PULL!

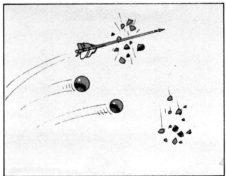

...AND THREE!

GOOD SHOOTING, PEG LEG!

STILL GOT YOUR ARM **AND** YOUR EYE, YOU OLD SOLDIER!

BAH -- IT'S MY **WEAPONS**! THEY DO ALL THE WORK. YOUR TURN, TJALL. DO OUR FAMILY PROUD...

PULL!

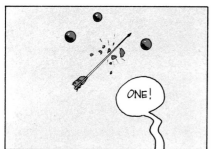

ONE!

...TWO!

GREAT, TJALL!

THANK YOU GENTLE PEOPLE! AND WHEN YOU'RE PLACING YOUR BETS TOMORROW, REMEMBER—

TJALL! WHY DON'T YOU SIGN US UP FOR THE TOURNAMENT INSTEAD OF STRUTTING ABOUT? WE'LL SEE TO THE HORSES AND THE WAGON.

...THREE!

FOUR!

A BRAVE HEART AND A FINE ARCHER... AND THE BRAINS OF A GOOSE! HEH. JUST LIKE **ME** AT HIS AGE.

NICE SHOOTING, TJALL.

KRISS! DID--DID YOU SEE ME?

MM HMM... I CAN HIT FOUR BALLS TOO. THERE AREN'T MANY--LIKE **US**-- WHO CAN.

HAVE...HAVE YOU ENTERED YET?

THEY ONLY ACCEPT COMPETITORS IN PAIRS. AND YOU KNOW SIGWALD WAS HURT. TOO BAD...

YOU KNOW, IF WE TEAMED UP, **WE** COULD BE THE BEST.

?!?

26

THE EVENTS WILL CONTINUE FOR TWO DAYS IN ORDER OF INCREASING DIFFICULTY. THE LAST TEAM REMAINING IN THE TOURNAMENT WILL BE DECLARED THE WINNERS...

SO-- LET THE CONTEST BEGIN!

GOOD LUCK, THORGAL!

YOU TOO, PEG LEG!

30

31

TCHAC

TCHAC
TCHAC

DON'T BOTHER -- THEY'RE NOT WORTH IT!

AS FOR THESE **BABES** WHO STROLL OUT OF CAMP UNARMED . . .

WE'RE EVEN NOW, AEGIRSSON! WE'LL SETTLE OTHER ACCOUNTS LATER.

MY THANKS ALL THE SAME.

FOR **WHAT?** YOU'RE MY PARTNER, REMEMBER? I'M JUST PROTECTING MY INTERESTS, THAT'S ALL. AND NOW YOU OUGHT TO TURN IN.

YOU'RE **TOO** KIND -- LOOKING AFTER OUR HEALTH TOO!

YOU WON'T FEEL LIKE LAUGHING TOMORROW -- NOT WHEN **YOU'RE** THE **TARGET.** SKILL ISN'T ENOUGH. YOU'LL NEED **COURAGE** THEN.